TABLE OF CONTENTS

W9-DEW-851

MONSTERS ARE EVERYWHERE!

And certainly everywhere in this book. If you're a fan of the unusual, unexplained, and downright creepy (and really, who isn't?), you've come to the right place! Get to know all kinds of strange beings, from werewolves to mummies to the chupacabra (the chupa-what?). And when you've had your fill of the monster info that's packed into these pages, give the ghoulish experiments a try. You'll make some monstrously cool fake blood, whip up a batch of some super slime, mummify an apple, and more.

SO, LET'S GET STARTED!
YOU DON'T WANT TO KEEP THE MONSTERS WAITING.

WHAT YOU GET IN YOUR KIT

YOU DIDN'T THINK THAT ALL YOU GOT WAS THIS AWESOME BOOK, DID YOU? CHECK OUT ALL THE OTHER GREAT STUFF THAT COMES IN YOUR KIT!

SLIME

When thrown into the face of an approaching monster, slime is the ultimate defense! (And no, your brother or sister is not a monster.)

HOW TO MAKE THE SLIME:
Add 2 Tablespoons of water and stir.

BEAKER

Use the beaker to complete your apple mummification on P. 16.

PIPETTE

The pipette can be used for several of the experiments in this book.

MUMMIFYING POWDER

Add some of this concoction to the experiment on P. 16 to mummify an apple.

GROWING BRAIN

How cool—a glowing, growing brain! The Frankenstein section on P. 10 will be very happy with this brain.

FUNNEL

Use the cool funnel to prepare your apple for mummification on P. 16.

4

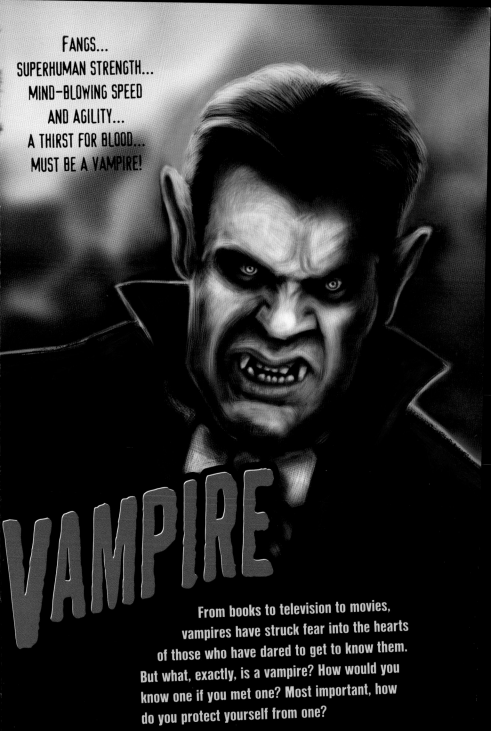

FANGS...
SUPERHUMAN STRENGTH...
MIND-BLOWING SPEED
AND AGILITY...
A THIRST FOR BLOOD...
MUST BE A VAMPIRE!

VAMPIRE

From books to television to movies,
vampires have struck fear into the hearts
of those who have dared to get to know them.
But what, exactly, is a vampire? How would you
know one if you met one? Most important, how
do you protect yourself from one?

A vampire is, quite simply, a being (alive or undead) that preys on living things and sucks their blood. It's believed that vampires can't cross running water, like a river; they don't have shadows or reflections; they can't walk upon holy ground, such as church grounds; and they can't enter a house unless invited in by the inhabitant.

So what can you do to protect yourself from becoming a vampire's next meal—which, of course, would transform YOU into a vampire as well? Legend has it that wearing garlic around your neck keeps these monsters away.

AND FOR THE GIRLS, THE TWILIGHT SERIES BY STEPHENIE MEYER CENTERS AROUND A YOUNG WOMAN WHO FALLS IN LOVE WITH A VAMPIRE. THE FOUR BOOKS— TWILIGHT, NEW MOON, ECLIPSE, AND BREAKING DAWN—HAVE ALSO BEEN MADE INTO MOVIES.

Should you encounter a vampire, however, waving a crucifix or rosary can keep the vampire at bay, and throwing holy water into a vampire's face can blind it just long enough for you to make your escape. Truly killing a vampire, though, requires plunging a stake through its heart. Do you have the guts to do it?

HEME IS A DEEP RED PIGMENT THAT GIVES RED BLOOD CELLS THEIR COLOR.

Is It Possible?

The idea of vampirism—of a person becoming a vampire—has been part of a number of civilizations for many millennia. There were tales in the folklore of the Ancient Greeks, Romans, and Mesopotamians of evil spirits and demons that were the precursors to modern-day vampires. A common thread was that there were several ways that vampires could be created. It was believed that vampires were suicide victims, witches, or those that were bitten by another vampire.

For those with a more scientific mind, vampirism is believed to be a disease. Porphyria is a disorder of the blood that causes a person to be sensitive to sunlight, which is a common trait of vampires. Some scientists theorize that sufferers of porphyria may drink blood to help with their heme production. A buildup of porphyrin on a person's teeth could make the teeth appear red, like bloody fangs. And this disorder can cause excess hair growth on the forehead, which may explain the appearance of the vampire widow's peak.

Make Your Own Fake Blood

WHOA. MAKING FAKE BLOOD. COULD THIS VAMPIRE STUFF POSSIBLY GET ANY COOLER?

What You Need

* TROPICAL FRUIT PUNCH (SUCH AS HAWAIIAN PUNCH)
* 1 CUP (236.6 ML) CORN SYRUP
* 2 TABLESPOONS (29.5 ML) RED FOOD COLORING
* 2 TABLESPOONS (29.5 ML) CORNSTARCH
* 1 TABLESPOON (15 ML) POWDERED COCOA
* 1 TABLESPOON (15 ML) CHOCOLATE SYRUP
* MEASURING CUPS AND SPOONS
* BLENDER
* GROWN-UP HELPER
* GREEN FOOD COLORING (OPTIONAL)

THIS RECIPE REQUIRES FOOD COLORING, WHICH STAINS. WASH YOUR HANDS (AND CLOTHES, IF NECESSARY) THOROUGHLY AFTER EXPERIMENTING WITH THE

What You Do

"Ask a grown-up to help you with this experiment."

1. Add enough tropical fruit punch to the blender so that the blender is a little more than half full.

2. Add the corn syrup, food coloring, chocolate syrup, cornstarch, and cocoa to the blender.

3. Turn on the blender and mix for 10 seconds.

4. Keep experimenting with the ingredients to get the color and consistency you want for your fake blood. If you need to make the blood thicker, add more corn syrup. If it's too transparent (see-through), add a little more cornstarch. If you want the blood to be darker, add a bit more chocolate syrup and cocoa powder.

SUCCESS!

YOU MIGHT NEED A FEW DROPS OF GREEN FOOD COLORING TO GIVE THE BLOOD THE SLIGHTEST HINT OF BROWN AND MAKE IT LOOK EVEN MORE REALISTIC.

FRANKENSTEIN'S MONSTER

Frankenstein, a novel written by Mary Shelley, tells the story of Victor Frankenstein, a brilliant scientist who builds a creature in his laboratory in an attempt to create a new species of humanoid. Frankenstein brings the monster to life, but when he doesn't obey him, he flees from the hideous creature in horror. Frankenstein's monster (also known as Frankenstein's creature) is human and eight feet tall, with thin, yellowish-gray skin pulled taut over his body; glowing, watery eyes; black hair; black lips; and large white teeth. He has superhuman strength, can withstand intense pain, and heals rapidly from injuries.

Perhaps the most gruesome aspect of Frankenstein's monster is that he is put together with parts from several human corpses! In fact, he has scars on his body where the skin is sewn together.

Is It Possible?

Hopefully, there aren't any scientists out there who are busy assembling humanoid creatures from dead bodies! But what about organ transplants? Doctors help to "rebuild" a person when they perform an organ transplant—that is, when they take an organ or organs, usually from a dead person, and put them into the body of a live person. There have even been people from around the world who've received facial transplants. In this case, the recipients have been given the facial features of a deceased person! In March of 2010, a man in Spain became the first person to receive a full facial transplant. And there are several others who have had a partial face transplant, where they've received a lip, nose, or other organ from a deceased donor. Not exactly Frankenstein's monster, but definitely a creation of sorts!

MAD SCIENTIST FUN

SO, WHAT EXACTLY IS ONE TO DO WITH A TOTALLY COOL, TOTALLY GROWING BRAIN LIKE THE ONE IN YOUR KIT? HOW ABOUT:

Grab a large jar (like a large canning jar) and fill it with Frankenstein's brain and some water. Then, watch it grow, grow, grow. You may have to add some more water as the brain gets bigger and sucks up all of the water. You can always add a few drops of red or green food coloring for a little extra mad scientist fun.

So, is the Frankenstein Monster real? Yes

EXPERIMENT #2:

Make Your Own Monster

TAKE ON THE ROLE OF FRANKENSTEIN AND MAKE YOUR OWN MONSTER!

What You Need

3 BOXES JELL-O (ANY FLAVOR)
BOWL
STIRRING SPOON
2 ¼ CUPS (.5 L) BOILING WATER
2 ¼ CUPS (.5 L) COLD WATER

13 x 9-INCH (33 x 23-CM) PAN
COOKING SPRAY
SHARP KNIFE
BAKING SHEET
2 SPATULAS
GROWN-UP HELPER

YOU'LL ALSO NEED A BUNCH OF ITEMS TO MAKE YOUR MONSTER:

* PEELED TOMATO (THEY'RE SOLD IN CANS THIS WAY—JUST ASK MOM!)
* TWO SLICES OF BREAD

* GREEN OLIVES (WITH THE PIMIENTOS IN THEM)
* DRINKING STRAW, CUT IN HALF

* MARSHMALLOW
* COOKED SPAGHETTI OR BLACK OR RED STRING LICORICE

What You Do

1. Empty the three packets of Jell-O mix into the bowl.

2. Carefully pour the boiling water into the bowl. Stir until all of the Jell-O powder is dissolved.

3. Pour the cold water into the bowl and stir.

4. Spray the pan with cooking spray. Carefully pour the liquid into the pan.

5. Let the Jell-O sit in the pan for about 2 hours. You want it to be slightly firm. A good way to check it is to try putting one of the olives in the Jell-O. If it stands straight up, your Jell-O is ready!

6. For the brain, press the spaghetti or licorice into the Jell-O near the top of the pan., Add the green olives for the eyes, the marshmallow for the nose, and the drinking straw for your monster's mouth.

7. Take one of the peeled tomatoes and put it in the center of your monster's body. You've just given it a heart!

8. Cut the bread into shapes that resemble lungs, sort of like this— Put one lung on either side of the heart.

9. Put the Jell-O in the refrigerator so it can get firmer, about 1½ more hours.

10. Cut a basic body shape out of the Jell-O. Cut a circle around the brain and face; cut a rectangle around the lungs and heart; and cut four small rectangles across the bottom of the pan for the arms and legs.

KEEP IN MIND THAT THE MORE YOU HANDLE THE JELL-O PIECES, THE MORE LIKELY THEY ARE TO FALL APART. SO, MOVE THEM ONLY AS OFTEN AS ABSOLUTELY NECESSARY!

11. Now it's time to assemble your monster! Use the spatula to carefully take the pieces out of the pan and put them on the baking sheet in the right place. For the larger pieces, ask your grown-up helper to use the other spatula to help you lift the pieces. Voilà—instant monster!

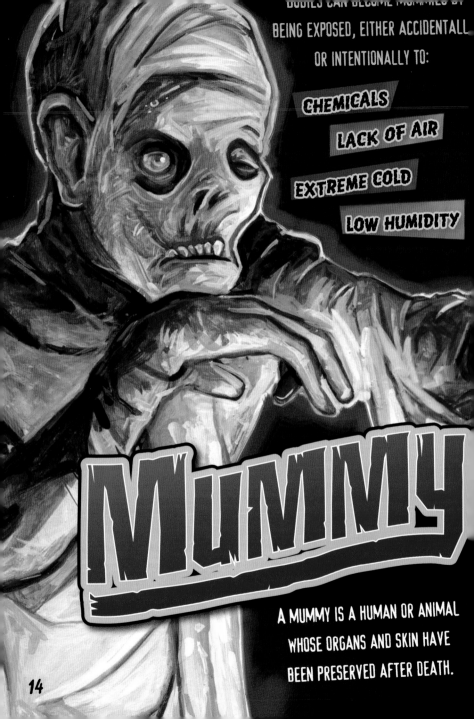

BODIES CAN BECOME MUMMIES BY BEING EXPOSED, EITHER ACCIDENTALL OR INTENTIONALLY TO:

CHEMICALS

LACK OF AIR

EXTREME COLD

LOW HUMIDITY

MUMMY

A MUMMY IS A HUMAN OR ANIMAL WHOSE ORGANS AND SKIN HAVE BEEN PRESERVED AFTER DEATH.

Civilizations around the world have been mummifying their dead for thousands of years. In fact, the oldest-known, naturally mummified human is a decapitated head that's believed to be about 6,000 years old!

So, how exactly do you mummify a body? Let's take a look at the way Egyptians mummified their dead. First, the body was washed with palm wine and rinsed with water from the Nile River.

A small cut was made on the left side of the body, and the embalmers—those doing the mummifying—took out the person's liver, lungs, and large and small intestines. A long hook was inserted into the person's nose and poked into the brain, which was pulled out in pieces through the nose. (Nice, huh?) Once the organs were removed, the body was covered and stuffed with natron (a salt found along the banks of salt lakes) and left to dry for about 40 days. After the body was dried out, it was anointed with perfumes and oils and considered to be ready for wrapping.

The full body was wrapped and painted with a liquid resin, which acted like glue. Then a cloth was wrapped around the body, and the body was put into its sarcophagus.

Is It Possible?

Well, we've seen that it's certainly possible for a dead person to become a mummy. But as for mummies coming to life, shuffling around with their arms straight out, and scaring the living daylights out of people, no way, no how. Once a person has passed away, his or her brain stops working. And a person can't walk (or do anything, for that matter!) without a working brain. So don't worry—while mummies are real, the scary, I'm-going-to-get-you kind are just a thing of the movies.

Mummify an Apple

TRUE, IT'S USUALLY PEOPLE OR ANIMALS WHO ARE MUMMIFIED. BUT WHO SAID YOU COULDN'T TURN AN APPLE INTO A MUMMY? YOU'LL NEED TO HAVE SOME PATIENCE, THOUGH; THIS EXPERIMENT TAKES ONE WEEK TO COMPLETE.

What You Need

* AN APPLE
* BEAKER FROM YOUR KIT
* FUNNEL FROM YOUR KIT
* 2 PLASTIC CUPS
* MEASURING SPOONS
* PIPETTE FROM YOUR KIT
* 3 TBS. (45 ML) BAKING SODA
* 3 TBS. (45 ML) SALT
* 1 TSP. (5 ML) MUMMIFYING POWDER FROM YOUR KIT

What You Do

1. Cut the apple in half, and then in half again.

2. Put one of the apple sections into the beaker. Put the other apple sections into one of the plastic cups.

3. Mix the baking soda and salt in the other plastic cup. Add one teaspoon of the mummifying powder from your kit.

4. Place the funnel over the mouth of the beaker. Pour the baking soda/salt/mummifying powder mixture into the funnel and over the apple section in the beaker. The entire apple should be covered.

5. Store the apples away from light and moisture for one week.

6. After a week, compare the apples. What do you notice?

What's Going On?

When a human body is mummified, all of the water is removed from it. In this experiment, by covering the apple in the beaker with baking soda, salt, and powder from your kit, you're helping to remove the moisture from the apple. That's why the mummified apple appears shriveled up and is smaller than the apples in the plastic cup. It also has brown skin after a week in the beaker.

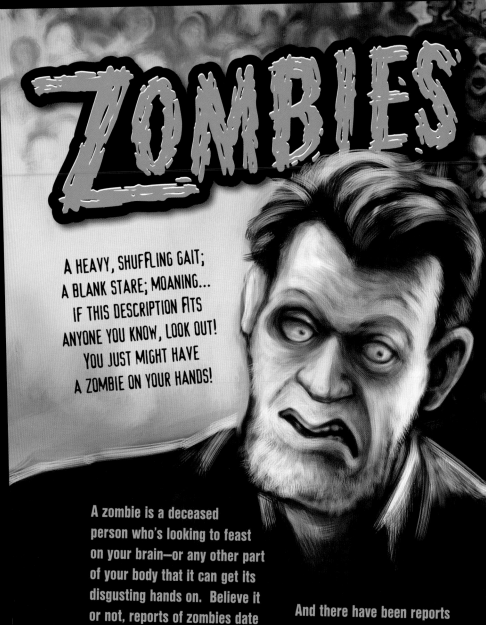

ZOMBIES

A HEAVY, SHUFFLING GAIT;
A BLANK STARE; MOANING...
IF THIS DESCRIPTION FITS
ANYONE YOU KNOW, LOOK OUT!
YOU JUST MIGHT HAVE
A ZOMBIE ON YOUR HANDS!

A zombie is a deceased person who's looking to feast on your brain—or any other part of your body that it can get its disgusting hands on. Believe it or not, reports of zombies date back many thousands of years. Coffins have been exhumed and examined, only to find scratch marks on the inside, as if the person had been trying to escape.

And there have been reports over the years from around the world of fishermen going out to sea, only to "catch" partially decomposed human beings that tried to jump into the boats.

Is It Possible?

Well, technically, no, because zombies are brain-dead beings. And we all know that a person whose brain no longer works can't function. But believe it or not, there are some people who do believe that zombies are real. They think that zombies are created when a person contracts a certain virus. This "zombie virus," as named by zombie expert Max Brooks, is called solanum. A person can also become a zombie by being bitten by another zombie.

So, how can you avoid becoming a zombie? Here are a few ways to steer clear of nasty viruses:

- Touch your eyes, nose, and mouth only when absolutely necessary.

- Cover your mouth and nose when you sneeze or cough!

- Wash your hands thoroughly with soap and water.

- Keep away from people who are sick.

Oh, one thing to remember: In case you ever find yourself in the presence of a zombie, the only way to destroy it is to destroy its brain.

EEK!

Zombie Slime

SHOULD YOU EVER FIND YOURSELF FACE-TO-FACE WITH A ZOMBIE (OR, FRANKLY, ANY OF THE OTHER CREATURES IN THIS BOOK), YOU CAN USE THE SLIME THAT CAME IN YOUR KIT AS DEFENSE! SIMPLY GRAB A HANDFUL OF IT AND THROW IT IN THE MONSTER'S FACE. THEN GET THE HECK OUT OF THERE! AND IF YOUR SLIME STASH IS GETTING DANGEROUSLY LOW FROM ALL YOUR MONSTER RUN-INS, FOLLOW THIS RECIPE TO WHIP UP A BATCH TO KEEP ON HAND. YOU NEVER KNOW WHEN YOU MIGHT NEED ANOTHER GLOB OF SLIME.

What You Need

- 2 CUPS (475 ML) WATER
- MEDIUM SAUCEPAN
- CUP (120 ML) CORNSTARCH
- STIRRING SPOON
- MEASURING CUPS AND SPOONS
- GROWN-UP HELPER
- GLOW-IN-THE-DARK PAINT, FOUND AT CRAFT STORES (OPTIONAL)

What You Do

"Ask a grown-up to help you with this experiment."

1. Pour the water into the saucepan.

2. Bring the water in the saucepan to a boil.

3. Add the cornstarch and stir.

4. If you're using glow-in-the-dark paint, add 1 teaspoon (5 ml) of the paint and stir constantly.

5. Take the pan off the heat and let the liquid cool to room temperature.

6. When you think the slime has reached slimy perfection, carefully scoop it out of the pan.

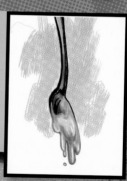

And hey, while you're at it, help to clean up the mess by putting the empty pan in the sink and filling it with some cold water. Your mom will thank you.

STORE YOUR SLIME IN AN AIRTIGHT CONTAINER OR A RESEALABLE PLASTIC BAG.

WEREWOLF

Legend has it that people become werewolves either by being bitten by another werewolf, being placed under a curse, or discarding one's clothing and putting on a belt made of wolfskin. These shape-shifters have superhuman strength and keen senses. And while they're sometimes likened to vampires, werewolves are definitely not vampires; they're their own, well, species.

Werewolf encounters have been recorded for thousands of years. In fact, the first recorded werewolf sighting reportedly took place in 1591! Just the rumor that a werewolf was running loose was enough to send the neighborhood into an extreme panic. People were afraid to leave their houses for fear of meeting up with the werewolf.

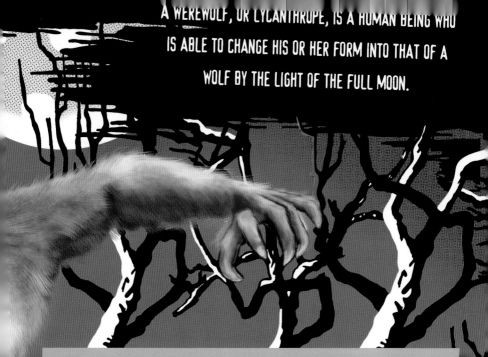

A WEREWOLF, OR LYCANTHROPE, IS A HUMAN BEING WHO IS ABLE TO CHANGE HIS OR HER FORM INTO THAT OF A WOLF BY THE LIGHT OF THE FULL MOON.

Is It Possible?

As crazy as it seems, yes—in a way. A person suffering from the mental illness lycanthropy believes that he or she is, or has transformed into, an animal, and the person behaves like that animal. Lycanthropy used to refer only to alleged human-wolf transformations, but today, the term is used to describe the supposed transformation to any animal.

There is also a disease known as hypertrichosis, or werewolf syndrome, where a person has an abnormal amount of hair growth on his or her body. He or she can have generalized hypertrichosis, which is extra hair growth over the entire body, or localized hypertrichosis, which is extra hair growth only in a certain area. And while there's no cure for werewolf syndrome, it can be controlled with hair removal.

So, are **WEREWOLVES** real? YES 👉 No 👈

WHILE IT'S PRETTY MUCH A GIVEN THAT MOST MONSTERS AREN'T REAL

(you don't really think there's still one hiding under your bed or in your closet, do you?), there are other monsters known as mythical—most likely the stuff of one's imagination, but without enough evidence to prove otherwise. Just enough doubt to make for an interesting conversation.

AND THAT'S WHAT MAKES LEARNING ABOUT THEM SO MUCH FUN!

MYTHICAL

MONSTERS

LOCH NESS MONSTER

PICTURE IT—YOU AND YOUR BUDDIES ARE HANGING OUT ON A BOAT
IN THE MIDDLE OF THE LAKE. THE SUN IS SHINING, THE WATER IS
SPARKLING. SUDDENLY, A LARGE ROCK APPEARS IN THE WATER.
WHERE DID IT COME FROM? IT WASN'T THERE BEFORE.
WAIT—IS IT A ROCK? AND JUST AS QUICKLY AS IT APPEARED,
IT'S GONE. YOU MAY HAVE JUST CAUGHT A PEEK AT THE ELUSIVE
LOCH NESS MONSTER!

Is It Possible?

Well, it depends on whom you ask. Those who claim to have seen the beast, of course, believe that they've in fact seen a plesiosaur, a large, prehistoric creature. Others need a bit more convincing. The case against the existence of Nessie is strengthened by the fact that one of the most famous alleged photographs of the beast is said to have been faked. Supposedly, the creature in the photograph is actually a small toy submarine. If you're a fan of all things Nessie, talk about disappointing!

Another argument against the existence of Nessie comes from scientists who've claimed that because of the body structure of real plesiosaurs, Nessie wouldn't be able to lift its neck up out of the water. Another argument explains away the beast as an underwater wave caused by earthquakes. And then there's the British Broadcasting Company (BBC), who in 2003 used sonar beams throughout Loch Ness to see if it could locate the supposed prehistoric beast living there. The result? Nothing. Negative. Nada.

BIGFOOT

Hairy, ape-like, six to ten feet (2 to 3 m) in height—with a description like that, you'd have to be talking about Bigfoot, or Sasquatch. This creature supposedly lives in the woods of the Pacific Northwest of the United States, although there have also been sightings reported in the Great Lakes region and the Southeast. Belief in the existence of a Bigfoot creature dates back to the mid-1800s, although much of the talk has come from folklore and is therefore nearly impossible to prove.

Is It Possible?

According to a large number of scientists, probably not. In fact, it appears that most of the information about Bigfoot has come from hoaxes, misinformation, and folklore. Some skeptics have argued that the creature is actually a type of giant ground sloth, not an ape. Others maintain that the creature is actually a bear with mange, a skin disease caused by mites. And when it comes to Bigfoot sightings, some people have gone to great lengths to attempt to convince the world that they've found evidence of Bigfoot, including dressing as large apes and using a set of large, wooden, 16-in. (41-cm) feet to make Bigfoot "footprints." In 2008, two men even went so far as to produce a "body" they claimed was that of a Bigfoot creature. But when the body was examined, it was determined that the hair on it was fake and the feet were made of rubber.

So, it appears that while a small number of scientists believe that the Bigfoot creature is a credible study, most have written it off as a hoax.

YETI

High in the Himalayan Mountains, located on the border between India, Nepal, and Tibet (now part of China), reportedly roams another large, ape-like creature. Known as Yeti or the Abominable Snowman, the beast is believed to be similar to North America's Bigfoot creature. According to those who claim to have seen Yeti, it is several feet tall, hairy, and walks on two feet, like a human.

CRYPTOZOOLOGY REFERS TO THE SEARCH FOR ANIMALS THAT HAVE NOT BEEN PROVEN TO EXIST.

So, is **BIGFOOT** real?   YES 👍   NO 👎

Other MYTHICAL MONSTERS

There are plenty of other monsters that are said to have existed. For example, Greek and Roman mythology are full of interesting, frightening, and just plain bizarre creatures. Here are four of the more well-known ones.

CYCLOPS

In Greek mythology, the cyclops was a one-eyed giant with immense strength. They were blacksmiths and metal workers and are credited with giving Zeus, the king of the gods, his thunder and lightning, and Poseidon, the sea god, his trident.

MEDUSA

In Greek mythology, Medusa was once a beautiful woman. But she angered the goddess Athena, and Athena turned her into a hideous creature with swirling, spitting snakes for hair and a gaze that could turn people into stone if they looked into her eyes!

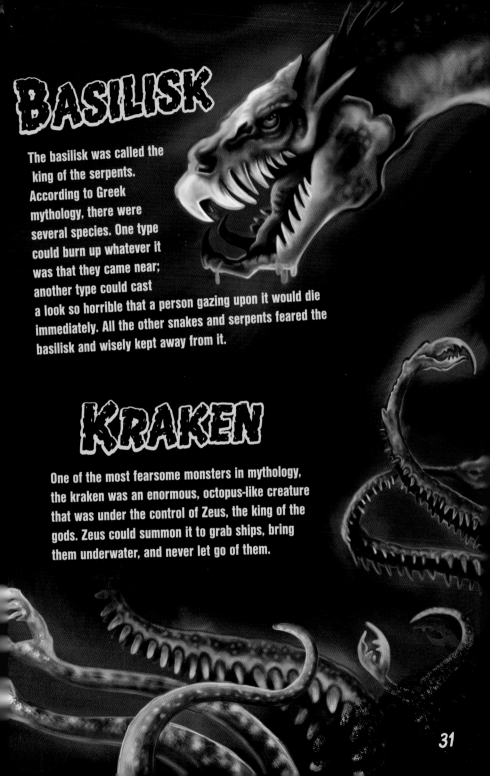

BASILISK

The basilisk was called the king of the serpents. According to Greek mythology, there were several species. One type could burn up whatever it was that they came near; another type could cast a look so horrible that a person gazing upon it would die immediately. All the other snakes and serpents feared the basilisk and wisely kept away from it.

KRAKEN

One of the most fearsome monsters in mythology, the kraken was an enormous, octopus-like creature that was under the control of Zeus, the king of the gods. Zeus could summon it to grab ships, bring them underwater, and never let go of them.

CHUPACABRA

YOU'RE A FARMER, AND YOU'VE TUCKED YOUR LIVESTOCK INTO THE BARN FOR THE NIGHT.

You lock the gate and head inside for the night. The next morning, you make a gruesome discovery: your cows are dead, lying on the ground with two puncture marks and trickles of blood on their necks. They've fallen victim to the chupacabra.

The chupacabra, literally "goat sucker," is a creature that's rumored to inhabit parts of Puerto Rico, Mexico, and the United States. Witnesses describe the chupacabra as reptile-like, with scaly, greenish skin, a row of spines or quills up and down its back, and a dog-like face with large fangs. It stands about 3 to 4 ft. (1 to 1.5 m) high and moves by hopping like a kangaroo. The creature was first reported in Puerto Rico in 1995, when eight sheep were found with puncture wounds in their chests, their bodies drained of blood. Since then, numerous reports of dead livestock, found drained of their blood, have been reported.

CREEPY!